PUFFIN BOOKS

LUNCH BOXES DON'T FLY

Michael Rosen was brought up in London. He originally tried to study medicine before starting to write poems and stories. His poems are about all kinds of things – but always important things – from toothpaste to chewing bus tickets!

Michael Rosen

Lunch Boxes
Don't Fly

Illustrated by Korky Paul

PUFFIN BOOKS

PUFFIN BOOKS

Published by the Penguin Group
Penguin Books Ltd, 27 Wrights Lane, London W8 5TZ, England
Penguin Putnam Inc., 375 Hudson Street, New York, New York 10014, USA
Penguin Books Australia Ltd, Ringwood, Victoria, Australia
Penguin Books Canada Ltd, 10 Alcorn Avenue, Toronto, Ontario, Canada M4V 3B2
Penguin Books (NZ) Ltd, Private Bag 102902, NSMC, Auckland, New Zealand

Penguin Books Ltd, Registered Offices: Harmondsworth, Middlesex, England

First published 1999
1 3 5 7 9 10 8 6 4 2

'Shut Your Mouth When You're Eating' reprinted from *Quick, Let's Get Out of Here*
(André Deutsch Ltd, 1983) copyright © Michael Rosen 1983; 'Tip-top tip-top'
reprinted from *Wouldn't You Like to Know* (André Deutsch Ltd, 1977)
copyright © Michael Rosen 1977

Printed in Hong Kong by Midas Printing Ltd

British Library Cataloguing in Publication Data
A CIP catalogue record for this book is available from the British Library

ISBN 0–141–30020–5

To the family chazzas – M. R.

··· Contents ···

Shut Your Mouth When You're Eating

Shut your mouth when you're eating.

   I am, Dad.

MOUTH!

   It *is* shut.

I can see it isn't. I can *hear* it isn't.

   What about *his* mouth? You can see *everything* in his mouth.

He's only two. He doesn't know any better.

   You can see all his peas and tomato sauce.

That's none of your business.

(TWO MINUTES GO BY.)

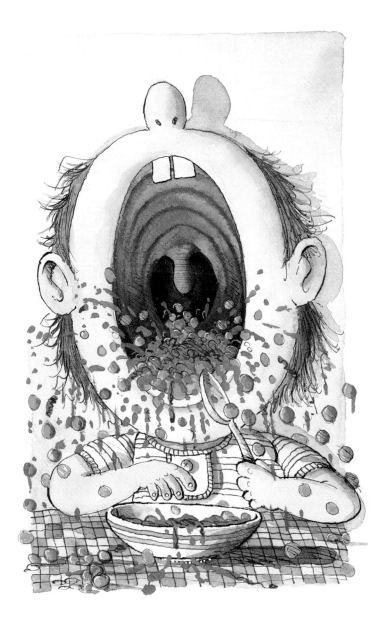

Dad.

Yes.

Your mouth's open. Shut your
mouth when you're eating.

It is shut, thank you very much.

I can see it isn't, Dad. I can see all
the food in there.

Look, that's my business, OK?

Peas, gravy, spuds, everything.

Look, you don't want to grow up to
be as horrible as your father,

do you? Answer that, smartyboots.

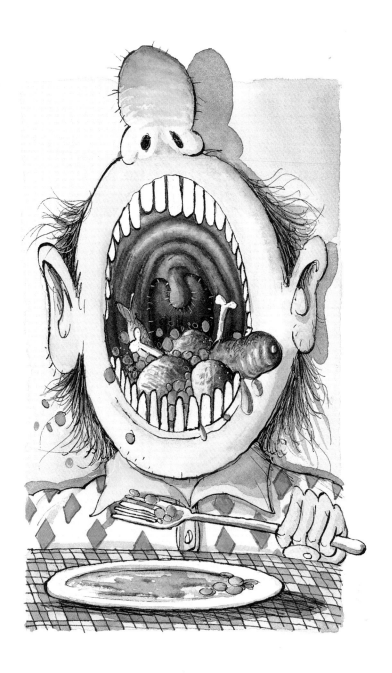

Ice Cream

I dream of ice cream
ice cream's a wow
ice cream's cool
I want some now

I scream for ice cream in the garden
I scream for ice cream on a tray
I scream for ice cream tomorrow
I scream for ice cream today

give a scoopful to a cat
give a scoopful to a baby
give a scoopful to a dog
give a scoopful to a lady

ice cream in a cake
ice cream in a cup
ice cream on the table
ice cream piled up

grab a slab for the outing
grab a slab for the fair
grab a slab for the playground
grab a slab for the bear

don't dance on your ice cream
don't fling your ice cream
don't sleep on your ice cream
don't sling your ice cream

lick it
nuzzle it
feel it
guzzle it.

Cake

I'm always awake for cake
cake is the tops
cut me some
cut me lots

make a cake like a truck
make a cake like a house
make a cake like a computer
make a cake like a mouse

give a chunk to a monkey
give a chunk to a fighter
give a chunk to a donkey
give a chunk to a writer

cake with candles
cake with a cherry
cake on a speedboat
cake on a ferry

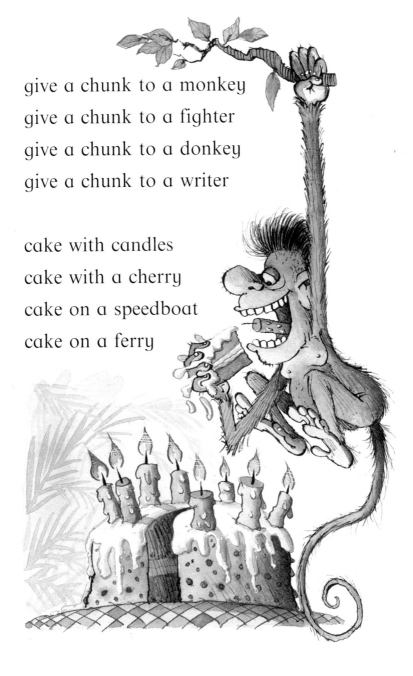

take a cake to a camp

take a cake to a cook-out

take a cake to a concert

take a cake to a lookout

don't squeeze your cake
don't soak your cake
don't rub your cake
don't poke your cake

mix it
bake it
cut it
break it.

I'm Funny about Honey

I'm funny about honey
I'm nuts about nuts
I'm awake for cake
I've got the head for bread
I've got the legs for eggs
I want rice in a trice
I dream of ice cream
I'd love to tackle an apple

I'll have it cold
I'll have it hot
I'll have it now
I'll have the lot

I want to shout
I want to roar
I want to yell
I want some more.

That Peach

Oh, Brian, that peach.

That was a peach.

It was the best.

The best peach there ever was.

OK, Mick. It was a peach.

Oh, Brian, that peach.

Waiting for me, it was.

Hanging on the tree

saying: pick me, pick me, pick me.

OK, Mick. I've got it. A peach.

The sun was burning me up, Brian.

And my mouth hated it.

My mouth wanted something wet
  and cool and sweet.

Something sweet and cool and wet.

OK, Mick. Yeah. Your mouth.

So I took it. I took it off the tree, Brian
and there was no waiting, no stopping
  me.
I got me teeth right into that peach.
Right into it.
Bite. Bite. Bite.

OK, Mick. Yeah. You bit it.

I bit it and

the juice just flushed out my mouth,

flowing around my tongue

juice on the loose, Brian

the juice of the peach.

That juice was the deliciousest,

   deliciousest.

OK, Mick. I've got it. The juice.

So what do you think, Brian?

Was that a peach?

Was

that

A Number One Peach?

I dunno, Mick. I wasn't there.

I'm a Cat

I'm a cat
and that's that.

I heard you say
I should be thinner.
I don't care.
I want my dinner.
Can't you see
I think it's awful
when you give me
a little forkful?
Can't you see me being grateful
when you give me
a massive plateful?

You see,
I'm a cat
that wants to get fat
and that's that.

Chewing Gum

Don't swallow chewing gum.
You can squash it,
you can wash it,
you can bite it,
you can fight it,
but don't swallow chewing gum.

You can make it longer,
you can make it shorter,
you can even squeeze it
underwater,
but don't swallow chewing gum.
You could use it to mend a broken bed,
you can balance it on the top of your
  head.

Listen!
If you really want,
you could take it with you
if **ALIENS** come to get you.
But I'm telling you now:
if you swallow that gum
I won't come and fetch you.

Don't swallow chewing gum.

Do you hear what I'm saying?
Don't swallow gum.
I know what I'm talking about.
I'm your mum.

Sandwich

I don't believe it:

he's not putting jam on his tuna fish,

is he?

He *is* putting jam on his tuna fish.

But why?

Why is he putting jam on his tuna fish?

I'll ask him.

"Why are you putting jam on your
   tuna fish?"
He's telling me he likes jam on his
   tuna fish.
No one likes jam on tuna fish.
But here he is
and he's telling me that he's
someone who is going to have jam
   on his tuna fish.

29

OK, OK, he can have jam on his tuna fish.

I'm not going to stop him having jam on his tuna fish . . .

. . . but have you ever heard of anything like it?

Jam on tuna fish?
Now I've heard of it.
First he puts the tuna fish on,
then he puts the jam on.
That's how he has it.
Jam on tuna fish.

I don't believe it.

The Truth

Are you wondering why
I'm dancing up and down?
Are you asking
why I'm rolling on the ground?
Do you think it's kind of odd
that I'm biting on a fork?
Do you think it's kind of weird
that it seems that I can't talk?

But it's my tooth – or my teeth –
between or underneath.
Beneath or between
there's a little bit of bean.

I'm telling the truth:
there's a bean in my tooth.
My bad luck:
it's stuck.

I Don't Like

Mum, Mum
I don't like
tame crisps in my shed
I mean
best rums in my crib
I mean
stoat bombs in my crest
I mean
creased tums in my bread
I mean
tomb crusts in my head
I mean –
what do I mean?

I mean
toast crumbs in my bed.
That's what I mean.
Mum, Mum
I hate
toast crumbs in my bed
toast crumbs in my bed
I hate them, Mum.

Sultanas

Dad says,

"Where are the sultanas?

Why are there no sultanas?

Who's eaten the sultanas?

The children must have eaten the
sultanas."

"Dad?"

"Mmm?"

"You've eaten all the sultanas."

"Did I?"

Dinner Hall

Everyone stop eating.

Stop eating and look at me.

At *me*, Darren.

I'm not on the ceiling, am I?

Sean, is that a potato you're putting
  in your pocket?

Well, I think it would be a good idea
if you took it out again before it gets
  mashed.

Now then, everybody –

and I mean everybody, Susan –

dinner times are just not good enough.

When I came in here –

Gemma, I said "stop eating" and that
  means

stop eating *anything* – even the water
  beaker.

When I came in here
I just couldn't believe my eyes.
Is it really such a big deal
that Mrs Gallagher has made
  chocolate custard?
I can't believe, Stephen, that your
  mum lets you put chocolate custard
on your chips
but that's what you were doing here.

And there were two girls –

no, don't look round,

eyes this way –

I'm not going to say who they were.

They know quite well who I'm

talking about.

There were two girls who decided

that Mrs Gallagher's chocolate

custard was really lipstick.

Rasheda – I know you're very proud
  of your
Superman Lunch Box.
It's not a bird. It's not a plane.
It's a lunch box.
And lunch boxes don't fly, Rasheda.
They stay on the table in front of you.
Hold it there.

If I hear the rustle of another crisp
  packet
I will ban all crisps for ever.
Which reminds me . . .
It's no secret, is it, that if you put a
  crisp packet
on the floor and stamp on it
it makes a bang.

So, football team, it's nice to see you
  all getting on so well together
but I'm telling you now there won't
  be a football team
if you try your "let's-jump-on-eleven-
  crisp-bags-in-a-row" joke again.
But today –
Darren, good – I've come off the
  ceiling but I'm not outside halfway
  up the tree either.

Eyes this way, please.

And today,

you know what I'm going to say
 next, don't you?

Yes, Zoe?

No, I'm not talking about the finger-
 nail you found in the ketchup.

I'm talking about the noise.

I said to you in assembly that it's
 OK for you to talk.

But, William, Abdul, Melvyn, singing
  "Come on you reds"
isn't talking.
I'm also talking about the way we eat.
Susan, tell me straight, did I, or did
  I not see you
sitting down with a dinner that
  consisted of
five baked beans and a chip?

Yes, I thought so.

You must eat more, my dear.

These dinners are very special

and Mrs Gallagher works very hard
   to make sure that

the food is good for you and tastes
   nice.

So eat up, and eat more.

And, Mark, that doesn't include you.

Yes, Warren?

No, that's true, none of the staff do
   eat school dinners.

We each have special reasons for that.

Mark, where Mr Holmes goes at
  lunch time
and what he eats or drinks is
  nothing to do with you.
OK, so your dad goes there too
but that's between Mr Holmes and
  your dad.
Come and see me later, will you?

Those of you who bring sandwiches in
can I just remind you again
that dinner time is not market day?
I'm not sure, Samantha, that it was
    fair of you
to swap a Milky Way for one Polo
    Mint –
no, Samantha, I'm not getting into it
    now –

OK, so it was three Polo Mints
but it's not the –
OK, OK, so it was half a Milky Way –
but I can't have this kind of –
OK, OK, OK, so it was three Polo
   Mints and a Flying Saucer –
but I can't have this kind of business
   going on in school.
Yes, Rasheda, I know his real name
   is Clark Kent.

And so to the matter of clearing up.

Darren, I'm not in the cupboard.

You know the routine:

leftovers in the slop bucket,

knives and forks in the bucket of water,

plates on the pile,

beakers on the trolley.

Is that so very difficult?

Why is it that every day

Mrs Gallagher finds

leftovers in the beakers

and beakers in the slop bucket?

Could you please make a special
   effort to get that right –
the beakers we can clean out
but the farmer who gets the slops
says the pigs don't like beakers.
Right now, everyone:
special effort and enjoy your dinner.

Hot Food

We sit down to eat
and the potato's a bit hot
so I only put a little bit on my fork
and I blow
whooph whooph
until it's cool
just cool
then into the mouth
nice.

And there's my brother
he's doing the same
whooph whooph
into the mouth
nice.
There's my mum
she's doing the same
whooph whooph
into the mouth
nice.

But my dad.

My dad.

What does he do?

He stuffs a great big chunk of potato

into his mouth.

Then

that really does it.

His eyes pop out

he flaps his hands

he blows, he puffs, he yells

he bobs his head up and down

he spits bits of potato

all over his plate

and he turns to us and he says,

"Watch out everybody –

the potato's very hot."

Tip-top tip-top

Tip-top tip-top
tap a speckled egg.
Once to put him in his cup
and twice to crack his head.